The Mys

Who Silenced Southsea's

CH00676581

In the summer of 1910, a strange character appeared on Southsea Common for the first time, who became an overnight celebrity and a treasured city icon; a mechanical laughing sailor owned by local handyman Quentin Price. Crowds were drawn from far and wide to hear the sailor's contagious laugh, and queues lined up to have their portrait painted with the famous mechanical star.

However, on the morning of the 24th August, as the local handyman was briefly called away to help fix a broken carriage wheel, someone forced open the sailor's side panel and destroyed its machinery in a terrible act of vandalism! Wires were cut, cogs were smashed, and water was poured into the machine, causing irreparable damage and silencing the distinctive laugh of the legendary jolly sailor forever.

Why would someone want to destroy Southsea's most iconic tourist attraction? Was it a personal grudge against the owner? Or did someone grow envious of the sailor's widespread admiration?

You must return to the scene of the crime, retrace the footsteps of key suspects, and finally uncover the truth of this legendary Southsea mystery!

The story detailed throughout this book is fictional, however the historical information and all extra details related to each clue is factual & based on detailed historical research.

HOW TO PLAY

1
Follow the Maps
to find the location
of your clue

2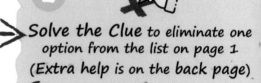
Solve the Clue to eliminate one
option from the list on page 1
(Extra help is on the back page)

3
At each stop you will
**Unravel more of
the legendary tale.**

4
At the end of your adventure your last
remaining items on Page 1 will
Reveal the final Secrets of the Mystery

IMPORTANT INFORMATION

1 On rare occasions, clues may be temporarily covered or permanently
removed. In this instance we ask you to use the extra clues at the back of
the book, and if possible, please report this to us.
It is recommended that you do the activity within 3
months of purchase, to reduce this risk.

2 Take care! You are responsible for yourself and your group. Be careful
crossing roads, make sure to respect old monuments and private
property, and if you are drinking alcohol please drink responsibly.

3 Any food & drink discounts available in this booklet are at the discretion
of the stated premises, and may be subject to change or cancellation.

Directions to Starting Point

The location of your first clue and starting point for this adventure is:

Portsmouth City Museum & Art Gallery
Museum Rd, Portsmouth PO1 2LJ

Once arriving at the starting point, your mystery adventure can begin!

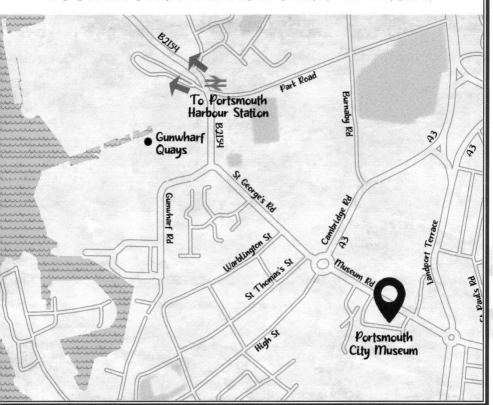

The suburb of Southsea began to develop in the early 19th century, as a growing amount of wealthy local gentry and high-ranking naval officers sought alternative accommodation outside of the cramped conditions that existed within the city walls of Old Portsmouth. The area was originally known as 'Croxton Town', which took its name from Thomas Croxton who owned the land but was renamed 'Southsea' (after the castle) in an attempt to rebrand it as an upmarket seaside resort. As well as advertising popular Victorian facilities such as a pump room, vapour baths, showers and a fashionable assembly rooms, visitors were lured to the new development by an official guidebook that once used the tagline 'Come to Sunny Southsea, where the death rate is only nine per 1000'.

Clue 1

Find the date of construction:

Symbols have replaced the digits, of the building's construction year. Work out the sums that sit below, and a time will appear.

:

_____   _____   _____

Eliminate the time

(Items placed together should be added)

ELIMINATE

(Extra help on back page)

Story

Quentin Price was born in 1872, into a family of ropemakers who all worked for the Royal Navy. However, long hours and backbreaking labour took a huge toll on Price, and after ten years of service he decided to quit, and set up his own handyman business in the wealthy suburb of Southsea. Mainly working on the maintenance of horse drawn carriages, Price quickly gained a reputation as a well -respected and hardworking tradesman, which opened up offers of high-paid contracts to work on the large villas that had popped up all over the area.

Directions

After you exit the museum gates turn right, and walk towards a roundabout. Continue straight, and then turn right into Great Southsea Street. You will see a small pub on your right called 'The Hole in the Wall' which is the location of your next clue.

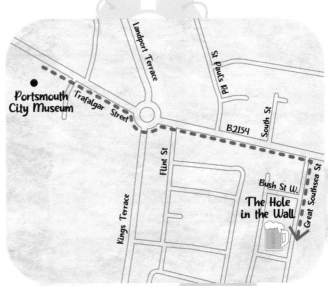

Hole in the Wall

Arguably Southsea's most famous resident was Arthur Conan Doyle, who while operating a doctor's practice on the corner of this street, penned his first two Sherlock Holmes novels ('A Study in Scarlet' and 'The Sign of Four'). Despite the huge success of his great detective stories, Doyle grew weary of the character, and decided to kill off Holmes in 'The Final Problem' in 1893. Fans of the books were so devastated by his fate, that some wrote objection letters to their local MPs and even to the Prince of Wales. Interestingly, Doyle's talents were not just limited to writing. During his 9-year amateur cricket career he successfully bowled out legendary batsman W.G. Grace, and was also the first ever goalkeeper for Portsmouth AFC.

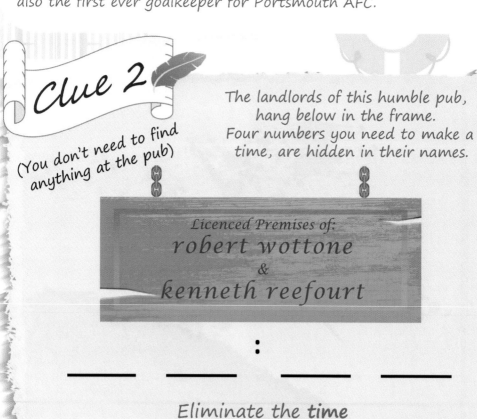

Clue 2

(You don't need to find anything at the pub)

The landlords of this humble pub, hang below in the frame.
Four numbers you need to make a time, are hidden in their names.

Licenced Premises of:
robert wottone
&
kenneth reefourt

:

—————   —————   —————   —————

Eliminate the time

ELIMINATE

Story

It was while working in the attic of a large villa that Price first noticed an interesting looking cabinet, containing a dusty old sailor and a mechanical box. The owner informed Price that her husband had brought it back from America while serving in the navy, and it had not worked for years. Price was intrigued by the machine, and immediately saw its potential to earn him a nice profit if he could get him laughing once more. Eventually agreeing a price for the old machine, the handyman wheeled the cabinet back to his workshop and began work on reviving the dusty old sailor.

Directions

Exit the pub and turn right. Your next clue can be found within the dotted area on the map.

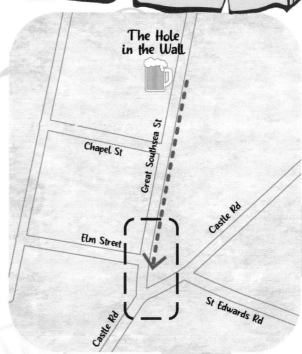

The Hole in the Wall

Chapel St

Great Southsea St

Castle Rd

Elm Street

Castle Rd

St Edwards Rd

Castle Road

Castle Road takes its name from Southsea Castle, which was where Henry VIII secured himself a front-row seat for the 'Battle of the Solent', and witnessed the terrible sinking of his flagship Mary Rose. The cause of the sinking is subject to much speculation, however the main reason has been credited to the change in wind speed and the failure of the crew to shut the gun ports when turning. It has been suggested however, that the rumour of Henry's position at the castle led the crew to rush to one side of the ship in order to catch a glimpse of their king, causing it to lean and capsize.

Clue 3

Look for something in this area.

It can be wound, and makes a sound,
a ring or often a chime.
Save the fate of an innocent man,
who hides <u>around</u> this time.

Eliminate a **suspect**

Story

After months of graft, the sailor had been cleaned and fixed, and his iconic laugh could be heard ringing out once more. Price decided that the best thing to do would be to sell his machine to a high-end department store, and arranged to meet the owner on Southsea Common for a demonstration. While waiting for the buyer to arrive, Price was approached by scores of people who wanted to hear the sailor's comic laugh, and within an hour he had gathered a full bag of sixpences. Price was delighted that the buyer never showed up for the deal; he had discovered a money-making machine that would become Southsea's biggest hit that summer and would make him a small fortune.

Directions

Join the small shop-lined street of Castle Road, and continue to the end until you reach a main road. Cross the zebra crossing, and look for a small fountain.

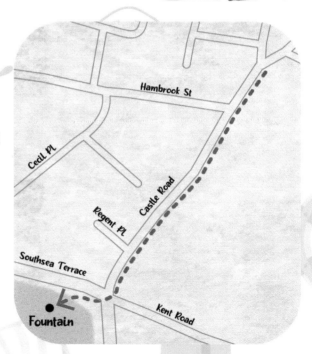

Southsea Common

The large area of open land known as 'Southsea Common' has been referred to as 'Portsmouth's breathing space', and has been used since Victorian times as a popular spot for meeting, strolling, fun and games. The puzzle as to why such a large amount of open space can exist within an area of such prime real estate, is that until 1922 the land was owned by the War Office, who wanted to ensure a clear line of cannon fire from both Southsea Castle and the approach to the old city walls. A special feature of the Common is the tree-lined path of 'Ladies Mile', which during the Edwardian era became a fashionable walking avenue for ladies dressed in their finest attire; an iconic scene captured in many of Southsea's vintage tourist postcards.

Clue 4

Match the colours to the missing letters, to create a word below.

BELONGING TO
THE
ROYAL PORTSMOUTH

YACHT CLUB

Eliminate a *golden object*

ELIMINATE

1:

Story

Throughout that summer, Price could be seen wheeling his sailor to the same spot, where queues of people would be waiting to have their portrait painted with the famous icon. However, on the morning of 24th August, everything changed. As Price was called away to help fix a broken carriage, someone secretly forced open the cabinet and destroyed its machinery, silencing the jolly sailor forever. Locals were outraged by this vandalism of their treasured mascot, and the local police vowed to severely punish those responsible. Was it merely a random act of criminal damage? Or did someone have a secret motive to put an end to the fanfare that surrounded the laughing sailor?

Directions

Head back to the main road, and join Western Parade (Carlton House on the corner) keeping the row of trees on your right hand side. At the end of the street turn left, and you will see a large building on the corner called The Queen's Hotel, which is your next stopping point.

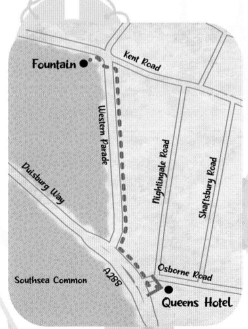

THE QUEENS HOTEL
20% OFF LUNCH (MON-THU)

Opening its doors to guests in 1865, The Queen's Hotel was one o
Southsea's first hotels, catering to an elite clientele who wer
attracted to the pleasures of the up-and-coming seaside resort
The building that stands today however was rebuilt in 1903 afte
a terrible fire destroyed the hotel and led to the death of two
chambermaids who tragically got trapped in the basement. Afte
its grand reopening, The Queen's Hotel once again became a
iconic local landmark, and has hosted a string of famous guest.
over the years including Winston Churchill, General Eisenhower
Beatrix Potter, and Rowan Atkinson- who took over the whol
hotel in 1992 to film an episode of his famous comedy, titled 'Mr
Bean in room 426'.

Clue 5

This mysterious note was left at the reception of the Queen's Hotel:

Your search to solve the crime is tense,
You start to think, it's not making sense!

Place the keys in the order that the symbol appears in the message to **eliminate a _time_**

ELIMINATE

(You don't need to find anything at the hotel, everything you need is on this page)

1

Story

Crowds of people were gathered around the sailor at the time of the crime, so somebody must have seen something! The first suspect to be identified was a local artist, who was close to the machine at the time, and was known to be critical of the sailor. For years this artist had spent his summers painting wealthy tourists as they strolled along Ladies Mile in their finest dresses, however, since Price's machine had arrived, all they wanted was a portrait with the laughing sailor! On the morning of the crime, the local artist was overheard cursing as Price wheeled his machine into place, and was therefore taken into custody as a key suspect.

Directions

Next to the hotel is a bus stop, which is on Osbourne Road. Continue straight, and turn right into Netley Road. As the road bends, turn right, and you will see a small pub called The Auckland Arms, the location of your next clue.

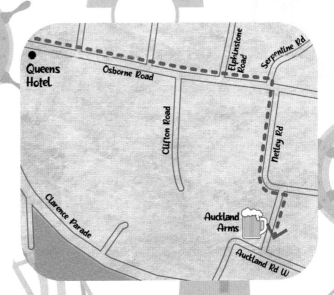

The Auckland Arms

As Southsea developed into a fashionable seaside resort, the city's huge class and wealth gap became even more apparent. By 1870, Clarence Pier had developed into an elite corner of the city, which was desperate to distance itself from the naked swimmers and 'promiscuous mingling of common folk' that blighted their view. The owners decided to erect a barrier to keep people at a distance, which sparked outrage among the population and led to 'The Battle of Southsea' in 1874. During the 4-day riot, locals destroyed the barrier and fought with police, armed troops were drafted in, and the official Riot Act was read out by the Mayor for the last time in the city's history. Despite the brutal crackdown, angry locals got their wish and the controversial barrier never returned.

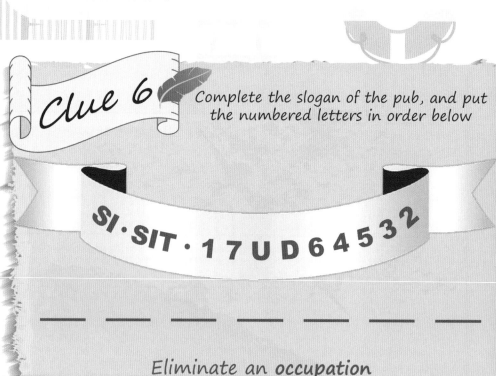

Clue 6

Complete the slogan of the pub, and put the numbered letters in order below

SI · SIT · 1 7 U D 6 4 5 3 2

— — — — — — — —

Eliminate an **occupation**

ELIMINATE

Story

The second suspect to emerge was Billie Brown, who was a well-known opera singer, and had been spotted close-by at the time of the attack. Billie Brown had an obsessive hatred of sailors due to her divorce from her ex-husband who was in the navy, and couldn't stand the sound of his mocking laugh as she walked by each day. Her husband had left her penniless after their divorce, and she had been forced to sing in the streets for loose change. While she eventually became a well-respected singer, she never recovered from the trauma of her ex-husband, and police believed it was this that caused her to silence the sailor in order to escape the daily torment.

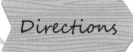

Directions

As you exit the pub turn right, and then right again, and follow the road until it emerges onto Clarence Parade. Turn left and keep walking straight, until you are able to cross at an island on your right. Follow Avenue De Caen (trees on both sides) until you emerge in front of the D-Day Story.

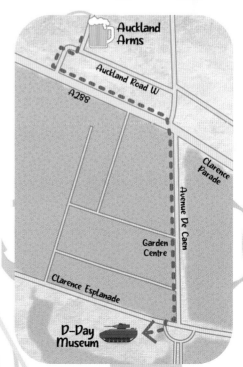

The D-Day Story

When the time came for D-Day in 1944, Portsmouth played a pivotal role as both the base for General Eisenhower and General Montgomery to plan the invasion and as the main departure point for the thousands of troops on their way to Normandy. The area became unrecognisable, as the beach was covered in barbed wire, anti-tank installations were dotted along the coast, and anti-aircraft guns took up positions across the area. In the run up to D-Day, due to the top-secret nature of the preparations, a ten-mile restriction zone forbid any visitors from entering the surrounding area, and local residents were required to show a special pass just to leave their house!

Clue 7

Look for a brick wall with many plaques

(Focus on the third wall from the left)

A famous name on the wall, shows <u>strong American spirit</u>. Use the letters below him, to fill in the gaps, and eliminate the person who holds it.

___ ___ Y ___ ___ N ___ ___ I ___ ___

One person is holding this item on the front page. Eliminate their **occupation**

ELIMINATE

1

Story

Police interviewed a number of passers-by in the hope of identifying more suspects, and one character that often came up was a juggling clown, who was seen loitering around that area on the day of the crime. Not much was known about this clown, however there was a rumour that it was in fact a local actress who regularly performed in amateur theatre productions. One local stated that 'before the laughing sailor had arrived, that clown was the centre of attention here. People would throw tons of coins into her hat and would fight to have their portraits painted with her. I've barely seen her around recently, and it seems like she's been forgotten'.

Directions

Next to the D-Day Museum is a double path with flower beds in the middle. Head to the end of this path, and you will see Southsea Castle in front of you.

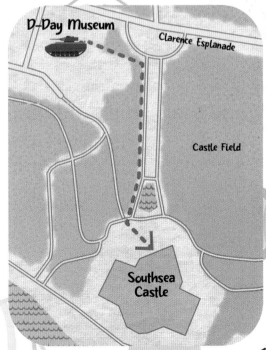

Southsea Castle

During the English Civil War, the Governor of Portsmouth George Goring, was a loyal supporter of King Charles I and attempted to hold the old walled town as it was besieged by Parliamentary forces. In the early hours of 5th September 1642, Roundhead forces decided to launch a night-time attack against Southsea Castle, and found it guarded by only 12 men, and a drunken Captain, who asked the troops to return the next day when he had recovered from his ale. Declining his request, troops jumped the walls and took the castle with ease. Despite Governor Goring's orders to fire the city's cannons on the captured castle, no damage was caused, and the besieged city of Portsmouth fell to the Roundheads only three days later.

Clue 8

Search the area of the castle to find the wording below:

The Royal (3)s commemorate improvements to (2) Castle (6)e in about 1683 (1) the direction (4) Sir Bernard de Gomme, Charles II's chief military engineer. They were moved from above (5) ori(7)al entrance to the present site du(8)g alterations to the Castle in 1814.

Place the missing words / letters in numerical order below:

__(1)__ _(2)_ _(3)_ _(4)_ _(5)_ _(6)_ _(7)_ d_(8)_ker

Eliminate a golden object

ELIMINATE

Story

After the loss of the laughing sailor from Southsea Common, attempts were made to find a replacement, however nothing quite got the same attention. Over the following months a range of new characters arrived including a mechanical monkey, elephant, and fortune teller, but none of them could fill the sailor's shoes. The only thing that came close was a performance by a local entertainer who dressed up as the old sailor and sat in a large box; laughing merrily and posing for paintings with wealthy tourists. However, while this was a good money spinner for a while, interest dwindled, and when the weather declined, the sailor was seen no more.

Directions

Head back down the path (the way you came) and turn right at the main road. Keep the grassy area on your left and follow the road as it bends around. You will see a large white building on the corner called 'The Jolly Sailor', which is your next stopping point.

The Jolly Sailor

A288

Avenue de Caen

Jack Cockerill Way

Clarence Esplanade

Castle Field

Southsea Castle

PHOTO STOP!

Take a photo

Tag on social media: @mysteryguides

For a chance to win a prize!!

20

The Jolly Sailor

The classic image of the jolly English sailor has appeared in print, art, and song for centuries, however, they haven't always been so merry. Just off the beaches of Southsea in 1797 a full-scale mutiny unfolded in protest against low wages, lack of shore leave, and cruelty on ships, at a time when the country was actively at war with the French. This dangerous mutiny eventually spread to London and became more political, with ships blocking the trade of the Thames and even declaring that they were going to sail to France to join the revolutionaries. While the mutiny in Portsmouth ended relatively peacefully, authorities cracked down on the actions of the radicals in London, sentencing 29 to death and hanging the ringleader Richard Parker from the yardarm of his ship.

Clue 9

Suspicious markings were scratched into one of the pub tables (below)

Use the table markings and the gold coins to create a word, and **eliminate the suspect** with a relevant surname

ELIMINATE

(You don't need to find anything at the location to solve this clue)

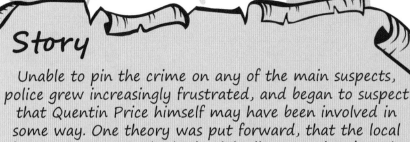

Story

Unable to pin the crime on any of the main suspects, police grew increasingly frustrated, and began to suspect that Quentin Price himself may have been involved in some way. One theory was put forward, that the local department store who had originally wanted to buy the sailor, had now offered him ten times more, but locals wouldn't let him sell up and move the machine away from its regular location. If it was to be broken in some way, that would allow him to cash-in on the laughing sailor, and escape any criticism or local protest.

Directions

Exit the Jolly Sailor and turn right, and head straight along Clarence Parade until you reach the entrance to Palmerston Road. Your next clue is somewhere on this corner.

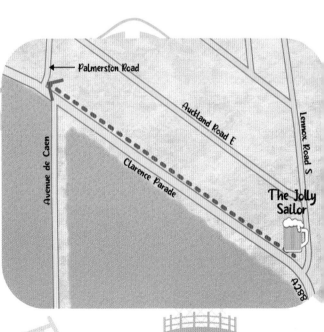

Palmerston Road

The street that you are about to enter is Palmerston Road, which takes its name from former Prime Minster Lord Palmerston, who is remembered for building the most costly and extensive system of defences ever undertaken in Britain during peacetime. Palmerston's Forts became the subject of much controversy at the time, as costs spiralled and the projects ran well over their deadlines. It was not just the cost that was controversial but also their effectiveness, as the forts in the north of the city had their guns facing inland rather than out to sea, leading many to joke that they had been built the wrong way round. With no further threat from France, these expensive and seemingly useless forts became known as 'Palmerston's Follies' and the name has stuck ever since.

Clue 10

Search the walls for your next clue:

An author by the name of 'Jane', wrote a book of this name:

Jane's _____   _____

Match the two missing words to two symbols below, to eliminate a suspect

 H   B   P   G   E   Q

Eliminate a **suspect**

ELIMINATE

Story

Conspiracy theories about Price's involvement were fuelled even further in the weeks following the crime, as the damaged sailor was sold for a big price to a large Southsea department store and appeared in the shop window just days later. How could he remove the sailor from Southsea Common and take it away from the admiring crowds? Price claimed that the machine was far more valuable to him on the Common, but was now unfixable, and he had no choice but to let it go. Price instead pointed the finger towards a local shoe-shine boy, who he claimed had a personal grudge against him, and was therefore the obvious person responsible for vandalising his machine.

Directions

Enter Palmerston Road, and walk straight until you emerge onto Osbourne Road. Your next clue can be found somewhere on this corner.

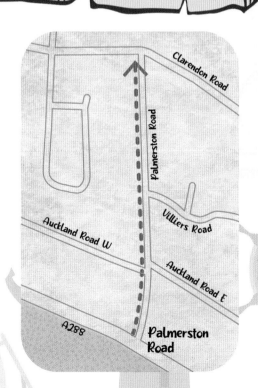

Southsea Shops

While Southsea has long been synonymous with fashion and retail, few are aware that Portsmouth was once an important hub for clothing manufacturing, with a particular focus on the art of corset making. During the Victorian age, corset making was big business in Portsmouth, as the wives of absent soldiers and sailors were left with no financial support, and were in desperate need of a steady income. By the 1840s a large portion of the city's population were employed within the clothing trade, which included a huge number of women working in corsetry. The city's most famous corset maker, 'Voller's', was established in 1899 and continues to manufacture corsets today, providing items to a number of famous names including Sophie Ellis-Bextor, Catherine Jenkins, and Madonna.

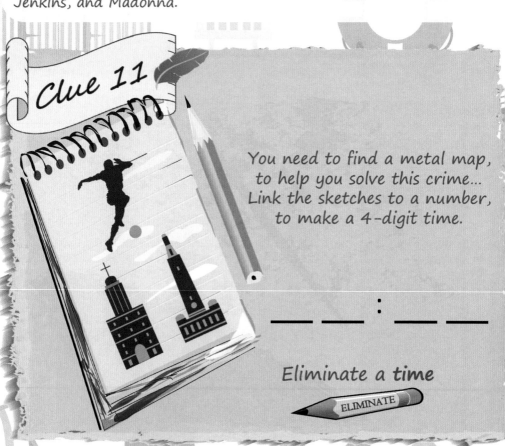

Clue 11

You need to find a metal map,
to help you solve this crime...
Link the sketches to a number,
to make a 4-digit time.

___ ___ : ___ ___

Eliminate a time

ELIMINATE

Story

This crowded and fashionable retail area of Southsea provided the perfect conditions for local pickpockets, who would single out wealthy shoppers and find subtle ways to relieve them of their purses. One particularly successful pickpocket was a local shoe-shine boy, who devised a clever way to snatch the valuables of customers as he sat them down to polish their shoes. On one sunny afternoon, as the pickpocket was snatching a purse, Quentin Price just happened to notice what was happening, and ran to the rescue. As the pickpocket was dragged away by police, he swore that he would get his own back on Price for turning him in.

Directions

Cross Osbourne Road at the zebra crossing, and walk through the pedestrianised shopping street until you reach the end. You will see a large church on the corner, which is the location of your next clue.

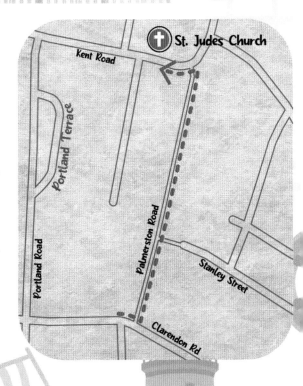

St Jude's Church

St Jude's church was built by 'The Father of Southsea' Thomas Ellis Owen, whose grand designs were influenced by his favourite architect John Nash, who was responsible for designing Buckingham Palace, Brighton's Royal Pavilion, and London's Regent Street. If you cross the road and take a left, you will see a row of impressive white villas known as Portland Terrace, which is generally considered to be the finest example of Owen's architectural style (see map). As a prolific investor, architect, and builder, Owen constructed 106 villas and 54 terraces in Southsea, many of which he kept for himself to achieve an impressive rental portfolio. By 1850 Owen was generating around £4,500 a year from his rental properties, which equates to around £620,000 a year in today's money.

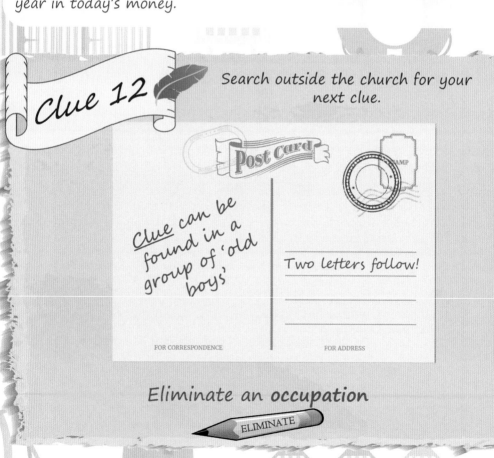

Clue 12

Search outside the church for your next clue.

Clue can be found in a group of 'old boys'

Two letters follow!

FOR CORRESPONDENCE

FOR ADDRESS

Eliminate an **occupation**

ELIMINATE

Story

As a way of punishment, the young pickpocket was ordered to serve time at St Jude's church, helping to mop the floors, tidy the bookcases, and clean the windows, which he grudgingly did for a number of weeks prior to the vandalism of the laughing sailor. Quentin Price claimed that it made perfect sense, that when the pickpocket had served his time at the church, he returned to the Common to smash his treasured machine in a terrible act of revenge. After all, he had been spotted on the common on the day of the crime, and he was particularly talented in the art of trickery and deception even in broad daylight!

Directions

Keep the church on your left, and follow the road as it bends around the corner. Continue straight along Grove Road South, and turn right into The Thicket (after the school). Follow the road as it bends right, and you will find a synagogue on your left hand side.

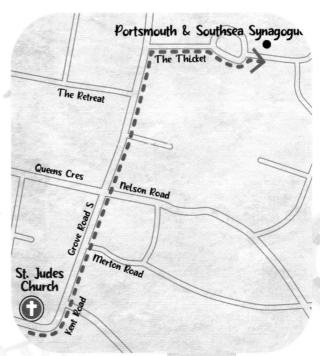

Portsmouth Synagogue

Another famous resident of Southsea was Rudyard Kipling, who lived nearby in Campbell Road. Kipling was sent to Southsea by his Anglo-Indian parents when he was only five years old in order to receive a British education, and lodged here with a local family. By the age of 42, Kipling became the youngest person to receive a Nobel Prize for Literature, had been the highest paid writer in the world, and had been offered the position of Poet Laureate and a Knighthood, both of which he turned down. As well as these notable achievements, Kipling is also credited as bringing the words 'cushy' (pleasant/nice) 'Squidgy' and 'Stinky' into popular use, as he was the first person ever to use them in print.

Clue 13

Your next clue can be found on the exterior of the Synagogue.

Find the parents of Avril Berman, and make an anagram of their surname.

Eliminate a **golden object**

ELIMINATE

Story

Seeing the laughing sailor moved to a large department store window and draped in company branding was not a popular move for proud Southsea residents. A campaign was set up by a regular of this synagogue to get the sailor reinstated on the Common, and an effort was made to raise enough money to purchase him on behalf of the city. Posters appeared in the windows of Southsea residents, and even the mayor got involved and attempted to negotiate with the department store for the safe return of the city's treasured mascot.

Directions

Continue along The Thicket, and as it bends left, turn right into Stafford Road. When you reach the end of this road, you need to cross the busy street into Albert Road (you will see shops ahead). Continue straight, and on your right hand side you will see some public toilets, which is the location of your next clue.

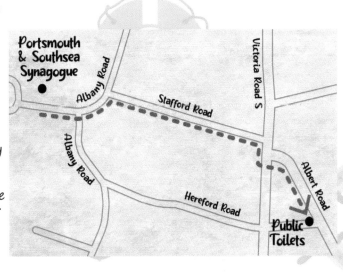

Albert Road

Thomas Ellis Owen originally named this street 'Wish Road', but by 1870 it had been renamed 'Albert Road' in honour of Prince Albert who tragically died a few years earlier at the young age of 42. Victoria and Albert are often referred to as 'the grandparents of Europe', as by the outbreak of World War One, their descendants ruled a number of Europe's monarchies, with the leaders of the three most powerful nations (Britain, Russia, and Germany) all first cousins. Perhaps Prince Albert's most famous legacy is being known as the man who introduced the Christmas tree to England in 1840, which however is a myth. 40 years earlier, Queen Charlotte, the German wife of George III had installed the first known Christmas tree at the Queen's Lodge in Windsor.

Clue 14

Find two murals on the wall of the public toilets.

Find the items in the mural, and match their position to a letter to **eliminate an occupation**

Story

On examining the evidence, the strongest lead came from the owner of an Albert Road hardware store, who claimed to have served the person responsible for the vandalism on the morning of the crime. 'That morning I served a strange looking person who appeared to be in colourful fancy dress. They had short hair and a lot of makeup, but I'm sure it was a woman. I see her a lot going in and out of the King's Theatre. She wanted to buy a pair of wire cutters and a hammer, which I thought was strange, as she hid them straight under her belt and nervously left without taking her change.'

Directions

Continue along Albert Road in the same direction, and you will see a large theatre on the corner as the road bends. This theatre is the location of your next clue.

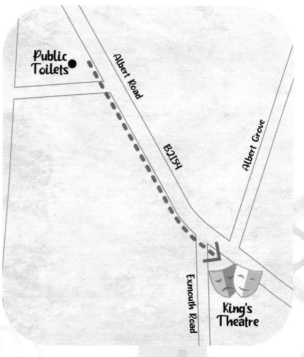

King's Theatre

This Theatre was built on an area of reclaimed marshland known as 'The Great Morass', which despite best efforts, has continued to be prone to flooding. Since its construction, a pump has worked round-the-clock in an attempt to keep the water at bay, however, there are legendary stories that when this failed, musicians had to use a small boat under the stage in order to reach the orchestra pit. Building large theatres on cheap, wet land was not uncommon, and a similar set up exists at the Palais Garnier Theatre in Paris, which is the original setting for 'The Phantom of the Opera'. The iconic boat scene where the Phantom rows across a dark lake is not a fantasy place, but an actual underground lagoon that still exists below the theatre today.

Clue 15

A host of stars you will meet,
not in the sky, but at your feet.
For George was bonnie, and
Richard was sweet, but Paul and
Penelope make it complete.

— — — — —

Place the first letter of each of the surnames of the people mentioned in the rhyme above (in order), to make a 5-letter word and **eliminate a golden object**

ELIMINATE

Story

The King's Theatre was a great place to launch the career of an amateur actor, as it was often visited by talent scouts on the search for new acts to appear in London's West End. So attractive was the prospect, that sometimes actors would fund productions out of their own pocket, and gamble their life savings on their own career. It was said that just a few days after the laughing sailor had been vandalised, an actress walked into the theatre and paid for a long run of her own Christmas production, with a huge bag of silver coins.

Directions

As you face the front of the theatre, turn right into Exmouth Street (you will see colourful terraced houses). Take the first left into Collingwood Road, and keep walking until you emerge in front of The Phoenix pub; your final location on this adventure.

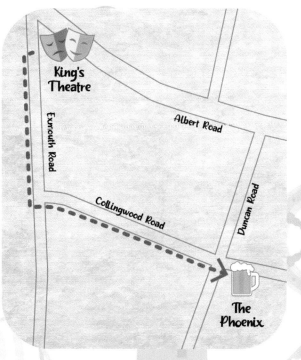

The Phoenix

10% OFF DRINKS

For over a century, stars from the King's Theatre have visited this pub for an after-show drink, arguably the most famous being Marie Lloyd, who in the early 20th century was known as 'The Queen of the Music Hall'. Despite her popularity, her risqué lyrics and suggestive winks got her into trouble with the national theatre censors, who attempted to ban her performances and imposed the use of large screens around the outside of theatres hosting her shows. At the back of the pub is the snug, which every year during panto season is transformed into a stable, and becomes the temporary home of the 'panto ponies' on behalf of the theatre. The bar staff dress up in costumes and lead the ponies on stage in what has become a charming Christmas tradition.

Clue 16

EAD

Your final stop is this actor's pub,
With a missing piece, of a ticket stub.
Pair it on the book's front page,
to eliminate a suspect, you wouldn't find on stage.

Eliminate your final suspect, who's surname relates to the word.

ELIMINATE

Story

Huge posters were unveiled on the outside of the King's Theatre to advertise that year's Christmas extravaganza, which was a glamorous dancing spectacular titled 'The Golden Phoenix'. However, much mystery surrounded the lead actress, and when interviewed, she said that she had accumulated the silver coins performing as a street artist; firstly as a clown, and then in a box as a laughing sailor.

Despite question marks over the show's funding, the production was a massive hit, and took the actress on a sell-out national tour and made her a large fortune. In an interview, the actress claimed 'This show is my life. I am the Golden Phoenix who has risen from the flames!'.

Turn the page for the final chapter...

Ellis Hall as The Golden Phoenix

While revelling in the success of her production, lead actress Ellis Hall was hiding a dark secret; it was she who had vandalised the laughing sailor in the fateful summer of 1910.

The arrival of that machine had taken away almost all of her trade as a street performer, and risked her plans to save enough money to fund her beloved show 'The Golden Phoenix'.

While the crowd were distracted by police chasing a local pickpocket, she took out the tools that had been hidden beneath her clown outfit and quickly damaged the machine before anyone noticed.

In the weeks following the crime, Ellis Hall transformed herself into the image of her victim, dressing herself in sailors clothes and laughing hysterically from a custom-made box, as her hat filled with stacks of silver coins.

As a finale for her widely successful national tour of 'The Golden Phoenix', Ellis Hall decided to perform the closing show at the King's Theatre in Southsea, in front of her home crowd.

Unfortunately, a huge wardrobe malfunction led to an extremely embarrassing exposure on the final night, that was made even worse by the fact that the audience was largely populated by sailors on shore leave. Ellis Hall was deafened by the sound, and haunted by the image of hundreds of sailors pointing and laughing at her, and felt that the ghostly figure of Southsea's mechanical sailor had returned to take revenge.

Forever haunted by that terrible experience on stage, Ellis Hall's theatre career came to an abrupt end, and she was never seen on stage again. A replica of the laughing sailor machine was eventually commissioned by the people of Southsea, and it was given a proud permanent place on the outside of Clarence Pier, where it continued to draw adoring crowds for over 100 years.

Enjoyed the adventure?
★ ★ ★ ★ ★

⊙⊙ Tripadvisor
○ ○ ○ ○ ○

Leave a review!